One evening, five learners arrived early at their numeracy class. They spoke about the problems people have with money.

Sonto said, 'Life is very difficult if you don't know how to add and subtract. It is very important, especially if you sell things to people on the street.'

'Have you ever sold things on the street?' asked Mary.

'No,' said Sonto, 'but one day I bought some things from a street vendor. Everything cost R5,25. I gave the vendor R10 and she gave me R5,75!'

'Did you give back the extra change?' asked Ma Betty.

'No,' said Sonto, and everyone laughed.

'You think that's funny?' said Ma Betty.
'Wait until I tell you my story.'

A farmer in their village asked Ma Betty
to help him plough his fields. 'I'll pay
you R50,' said the farmer.

'It's peanuts, but I'll do it,' said Ma Betty.

When the ploughing was done, the
farmer gave Ma Betty a R50 note.
'What's this?' asked Ma Betty.

'This is R50,' said the farmer.

'You can't fool me,' said Ma Betty.
'I know what fifty rand looks like!'

'This *is* R50,' said the farmer again.

But Ma Betty now wanted to be paid in coins. In the end the farmer gave her a big pile of coins. The next evening her daughter counted the money for her.

'Oh, Ma,' she cried. 'It's only R27!'

Ma Betty was very angry.

'That really is peanuts,' she said.

Bra Themba said, 'We must all learn to work with money. Two years ago, I worked at a shop in town. There the boss found out that I was sharp. He told me to add all the arrears.'

'Arrears! What does that mean?' asked Mary.

'Sometimes a customer owes money'
said Bra Themba. 'But she can pay it off
every month. If she does not pay one
month, then that is called arrears. We
then say that person is in arrears.'

'Bra Themba,' asked David, 'how did you add all those arrears?'

'Oh,' said Bra Themba, 'I did quick counting. Don't you know about a calculator?' He took out a calculator and showed them.

David said, 'I was in arrears last month. I am paying off my new furniture. I earn enough money to pay off my furniture every month. But last month I spent my money on useless things. So I tried to change the way I work with money.'

David then told his story.

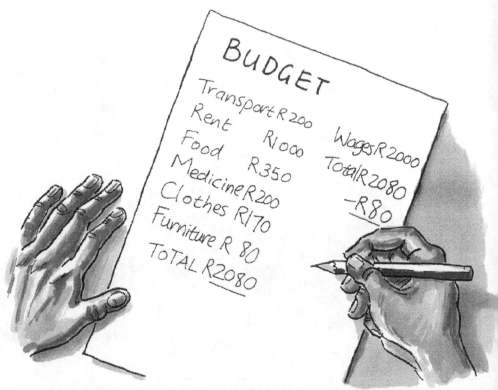

BUDGET

Transport R 200
Rent   R 1 000
Food   R 350
Medicine R 200
Clothes R 170
Furniture R 80
TOTAL R 2080

Wages R 2000
Total R 2080
    − R 80

David decided to do a monthly budget.
He added up how much money he
needed for rent, food, transport and
other things. Then he subtracted that
amount from his wages to see how
much money was left over. But there
was nothing left over!

'I'm sorry,' David told his wife, 'I've done my budget, but there is no money to pay for the furniture.'

'I think you didn't count properly,' said his wife. 'You made a mistake.'

'I think you're right,' said David. 'I'll break my budget and pay for the furniture first.'

'This budget!' his wife sighed. 'It's making my head sore. You must never do it again!'

'My story makes my head sore also,'
said Mary. 'Listen to this.'

One day Mary went to the shop to buy
some groceries. She had R40 to spend.
She bought all the things she needed.

When Mary got home, she gave her
mother the change to keep. 'How much
did you spend on all these things?'
asked her mother.

'R22,55,' said Mary.

'This change is wrong. It's only R7,45,'
said Mary's mother.

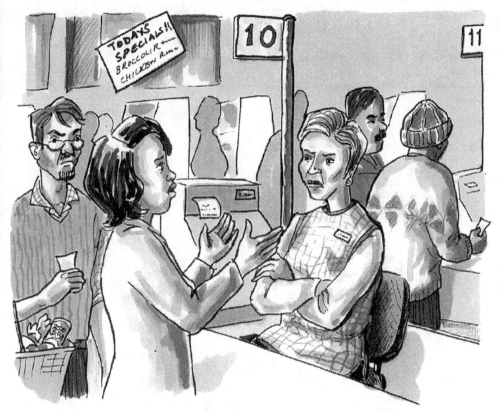

'Oh, no!' cried Mary, and she ran all the way back to the shop.

'Did you get your money back?' asked Sonto.

'No,' said Mary. Everyone sighed.

'Well,' said Ma Betty, 'we are making the right change in our lives when we come here to learn.' She laughed. 'And we are making sure that from now on we will always get the right change!'